Work Together

By Lisa Walston   Illustrated by Mike Dammer

Target Skill Letter Recognition *Ff, Gf, Hh, Ii, Jj, Kk, Ll, Mm, Nn*
High-Frequency Words *I, am*

PEARSON
Scott
Foresman

I am Cat.

 I am Dog.

I am Mom.

4

 I am Mom.

I am hammering.

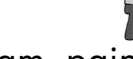

I am painting.

I am happy.